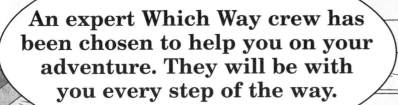

An expert Which Way crew has been chosen to help you on your adventure. They will be with you every step of the way.

Table of Contents

Noah Zark is a zookeeper who loves animals so much that he always brings one on his adventures. For this trip, he has brought Little Bill the buffalo.

Little Bill can't wait to visit some of his buffalo buddies in the large herd in Custer State Park.

WHO is heading for the WHICH WAY HALL OF FAME?

WHAT will be in the WHICH WAY MUSEUM?

WHERE will the WHICH WAY SUPERMAX MOVIE be filmed?

Sioux Falls Calls

The crew starts their South Dakota trek in Sioux Falls, at the very eastern end of the state. Long ago, Native Americans camped near the beautiful falls of the Big Sioux River. In the 1800s, pioneers called the town that sprang up here Sioux Falls, after the roaring waterfall. Today, this fast-growing city is the largest in the state.

The crew decides to go to Falls Park. From here they enjoy a great view of the river and the falls. If you look closely, you will see pictures hidden in and around the swirling waters. Find them all to get off to a great start. When you're done, check the bottom of page 3.

Strike out the
baseball manager.

Edit out the
newspaper owner.

Cross off the chief.

Scrap the scientist.

Dismiss the
sharpshooter.

Erase the writer.

Have you found all of the hidden
items? One object is hidden twice.
When you find that object, look at the
instructions under it. Turn to page 28
and use the clue to eliminate your
first South Dakotan.

One in Vermillion

The crew drives south on Interstate 29. Your next stop is Vermillion. The word *vermillion* describes a bright shade of red. The town has this colorful name because of the red clay on which it is built.

One of the more unexpected sites is the America's Shrine to Music Museum. It holds one of the world's largest collections of old and rare musical instruments. More than 10,000 instruments are on display here. According to Rhonda, they include a rare violin made by Antonio Stradivari.

The crew wanders through the exhibits. Meanwhile, you must take note of an important clue. Use the letters next to each instrument to solve the picture code. When you finish, waltz over to the bottom of page 5.

Did you crack the code? Now turn to page 28 and do what the clue says.

Li'l Town on the Prairie

Tess turns the Which Way wheels north on Interstate 29, then west on Route 14, heading for De Smet. Author Laura Ingalls Wilder moved here as a child. Her famous *Little House* books tell about frontier life in and near this prairie town. According to Rhonda, 18 of the sites mentioned in the books can still be seen.

When the crew arrives, the Laura Ingalls Wilder pageant is in full swing. Every year the town celebrates its hometown author. There are parades plus demonstrations of pioneer activities, such as quilt-making and hay-twisting. As the crew wanders through town, use the clues to look for letters. Find each letter, then write it in the box at the bottom of page 7.

1. The first letter is on a sunbonnet.
2. The second letter is beside a wagon wheel.
3. A blacksmith has the third letter.
4. You'll find a woman sewing the fourth letter.
5. A horse has the fifth letter.
6. You'll find the sixth letter on a fence post.
7. The seventh letter is on a door behind Noah.
8. A farmer has the eighth letter.
9. The ninth letter is in a tree.

Did you find all the letters? On page 28, cross off

___ ___ ___ ___ ___ ___ ___ ___ ___ .
1   2   3   4   5   6   7   8   9

TOWN CROSSINGS

The Which Way wheels continue north. The crew soon arrives at Watertown. Alex checks the map and realizes that this is the perfect name for this town. It is surrounded by lakes. The lakes in this part of the state were carved by glaciers more than 20,000 years ago.

The crew decides to cool off before continuing. Tess parks at a lakeside park. Everyone jumps out for a picnic lunch and a swim. Even Little Bill tries the dog paddle, buffalo style!

This is a good time for you to dive into your map and collect some facts about South Dakota. Fill in the answers, then float over to the bottom of page 9 for your next clue.

Don't Forget Your Map!
All the places in the puzzle can be found on your map of South Dakota.

ACROSS

3. Look south of South Dakota to find this border state.

4. This Corn Palace town is near I-90 between Sioux Falls and the Missouri River.

7. You'll find the largest city in South Dakota near where Interstates 90 and 29 meet.

9. There are no losers in this town near where Route 18 meets Route 183.

DOWN

1. This town is west of Junction City, near the Nebraska border.

2. This town on I-90 is between Wasta and Cactus Flat.

5. You'll see this town at the junction of Routes 14 and 37.

6. The state capital is on the Missouri River where Routes 34 and 14 meet.

8. This Black Hills town lies between Spearfish and Rapid City.

Did you find all the places?
Some of the letters are in shaded boxes.
Write them here.

___ ___ ___ ___ ___ ___ ___ ___ ___

Now unscramble the letters to eliminate

___ ___ ___ ___ ___ ___ ___ ___

from the list on page 28.

9

Once Upon a Time

The crew climbs back into the Which Way wagon. The next stop is the city of Aberdeen. One of the town's most famous citizens was newspaper editor L. Frank Baum. He lived here in the late 1800s. Years later he became famous as the author of *The Wonderful Wizard of Oz*.

Rhonda wants to follow the yellow brick road into Storybook Land. This theme park features scenes from Oz and other famous children's stories. Alex starts to make a list of his favorite stories. But his hard drive is having a hard time giving him the answers. Look at each clue on his laptop. Then unscramble the name of the story or storybook character that it describes. When you've reached THE END, go to the box on page 11.

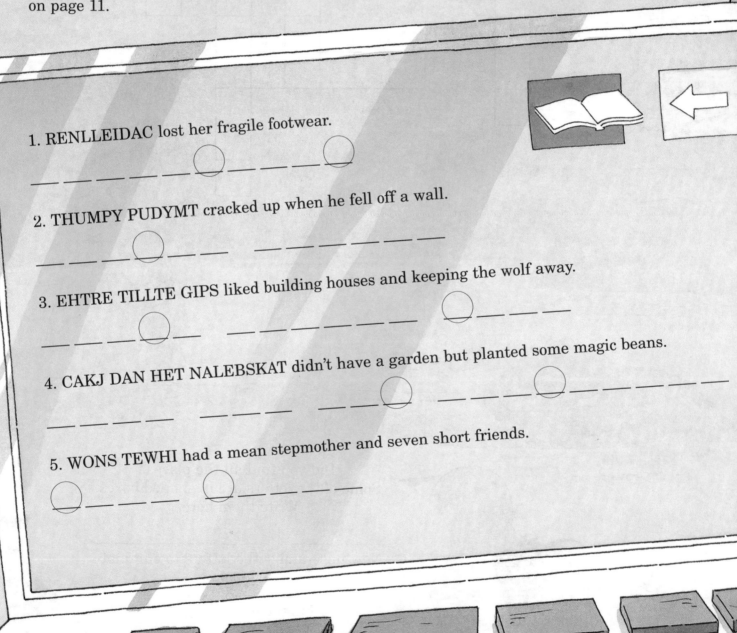

1. RENLLEIDAC lost her fragile footwear.

__ __ __ (__) __ __ __ (__) __ __ __

2. THUMPY PUDYMT cracked up when he fell off a wall.

__ __ (__) __ __ __   __ __ __ __ __ __

3. EHTRE TILLTE GIPS liked building houses and keeping the wolf away.

__ __ (__) __ __ __   __ __ __ __ __ (__) __ __ __

4. CAKJ DAN HET NALEBSKAT didn't have a garden but planted some magic beans.

__ __ __ __   __ __ __   __ __ (__) __   __ __ __ (__) __ __ __ __ __

5. WONS TEWHI had a mean stepmother and seven short friends.

(__) __ __ __   (__) __ __ __ __ __

Did you unscramble the names? Some letters are circled. Write them here:

___ ___ ___ ___ ___ ___ ___ ___ ___

Now unscramble these letters to reveal someone on page 28 who is associated with a

___ ___ ___ ___ ___ ___ ___ ___ ___.

Cross this person off the list.

Can't Pop This!

Tess turns south onto Route 281 toward Mitchell. The small town's big claim to fame is the world-famous Corn Palace. It was built in 1892 to encourage pioneers to settle there. Every year artists use thousands of ears of corn and other grains to make huge murals on the outside walls.

Rhonda pops out of the Which Way wagon for a closer look. She's in luck—an artist is working on a picture. Watching the artist work with all that corn makes Rhonda think of food. Help her remember some foods made with corn. Then pop over to the box on page 13.

A popular breakfast cereal   CORN __ __ __ __ __ __ __ __
1

Crunchy snack food great for dipping   CORN __ __ __ __ __
2

A sweet breakfast treat   CORN __ __ __ __ __ __ __
3

The way to eat an ear of corn   CORN __ __ __ __ __ __ __ __ __
4   5

A thick soup that rhymes with "powder"   CORN __ __ __ __ __ __
6

A hot movie treat __ __ __ __ __ __ __ __ __ __ __ __ CORN
7

Deep-fried frankfurter on a stick   CORN __ __ __
8

MITCHELL CORN PALACE

→ SOUTH DAKOTA ←

Did you discover all the foods made with corn?
Some of the letters have numbers underneath.
Write them in the spaces below.

Write the words ___ ___ ___ ___ ___   ___ ___ ___ ___ on page 29.
                   5   1   8   3   4   6   3   7   2

Sioux Clue

The crew members return to the road. They cross the Missouri River and continue west on Interstate 90. Soon they see signs for a Native American powwow. Many Sioux tribes live on reservations in South Dakota. Every year they hold powwows that celebrate their heritage.

Tess turns south, and pretty soon the crew is right in the middle of a huge powwow on the Rosebud Reservation. There's so much to see that Noah grabs a brochure. It has pictures of all the things that can be found at the powwow. But wait! One of the objects in the brochure is NOT in the picture. When you find out which one it is, dance down to the box on page 15.

THE FIFTH T

THE THIRD F

THE FIRST D

THE SIXTH B

THE THIRD G

THE FIRST A

THE FIRST H

Did you discover which object isn't at
the powwow? There are some words underneath
the picture of that item; write them
in the spaces below.

On page 29, write the words

——— — ———— —— —— ————   .

15

Hitting the Wall

The crew continues northwest. The next stop is the town of Wall. In the 1930s, the owners of the Wall Drug Store gave away free ice water to drum up business. It worked! Today more than 20,000 people come to the store each day during the summer.

Little Bill and Noah walk over to the nearby National Grasslands Visitor Center. They want to gather some information on the state's plains. Meanwhile, the rest of the crew goes into the store. Wall Drug is full of interesting things. After the crew looks at an eighty-foot dinosaur, listens to a cowboy band, and gazes at a replica of Mount Rushmore, they split up and start shopping.

Each crew member has $20.00 to spend. Look at each person's shopping list and add up the purchases. When you're done, go to the bottom of page 17.

Rhonda's list

5 postcards @ .50 each	$ 2.50
cowboy hat	$10.50
feather earrings	$ 5.25
ice-cream cone	$ 1.50
Total	$

Alex's list

Book of Prairie Facts	$ 3.50
cowboy belt buckle	$15.00
milkshake	$ 1.50
Total	$

Tess's list

T-shirt	$ 5.75
carving of an Indian chief	$ 2.25
poster of the prairie	$ 8.50
box of fudge	$ 2.50
Total	$

Did you add up the prices? Which crew member had the most money left over?

If it was Rhonda, the clue is CROSS OFF THE.

If it was Tess, the clue is AND CIRCLE EVERY.

If it was Alex, the clue is SKIP OVER EACH.

Now turn to page 29 and write the clue.

You Herd That

Little Bill is anxious to see his relatives, so the crew decides to split up. Noah and Little Bill catch a ride to Custer State Park. Meanwhile, the rest of the crew will explore Badlands National Park. Everyone will meet at Mount Rushmore later.

Noah and Bill continue west to Rapid City and then head south on Route 79. At the edge of Black Hills National Forest, they reach their destination. Little Bill is so excited! One of America's largest buffalo herds lives in Custer State Park.

Little Bill spots his cousins and runs off. While he's gone, you can round up a few South Dakota facts. When you've herded all the facts together, stampede down to the box on page 19.

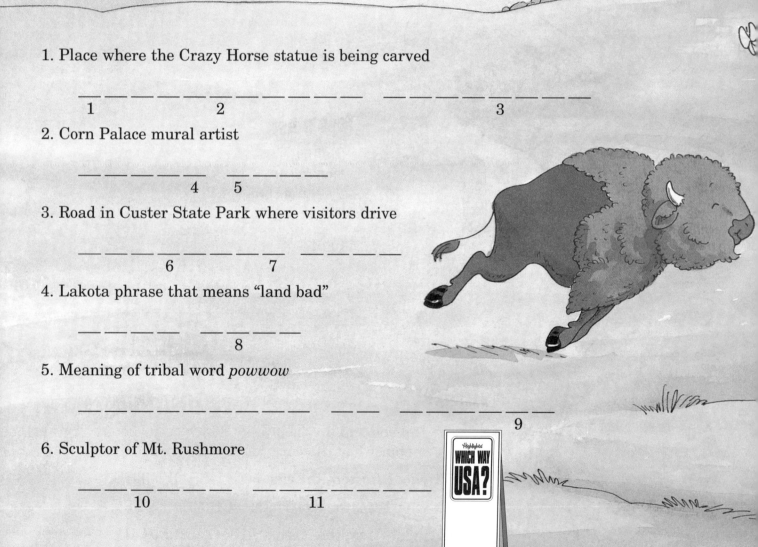

1. Place where the Crazy Horse statue is being carved

___ ___ ___ ___ ___ ___ ___ ___ ___   ___ ___ ___ ___ ___ ___
   1   2   3

2. Corn Palace mural artist

___ ___ ___ ___ ___   ___ ___ ___ ___
      4   5

3. Road in Custer State Park where visitors drive

___ ___ ___ ___ ___ ___ ___   ___ ___ ___ ___
       6   7

4. Lakota phrase that means "land bad"

___ ___ ___ ___   ___ ___ ___ ___
       8

5. Meaning of tribal word *powwow*

___ ___ ___ ___ ___ ___ ___ ___   ___ ___   ___ ___ ___ ___ ___
                                9

6. Sculptor of Mt. Rushmore

___ ___ ___ ___ ___ ___   ___ ___ ___ ___ ___
    10   11

Highlights
WHICH WAY
USA?

STATE MAP

18

Don't Forget Your Map!
You can round up the answers to this puzzle by looking at the *back* of your South Dakota map.

Did you fill in the answers? There are numbers under some of the letters. Write those letters in the spaces below.

On page 29, write the words

___ ___ ___ ___ ___   ___ ___ ___ ___ ___ ___ .
10 5   8   4   6   9   2   1   3   7   11

Bad but Beautiful

Meanwhile, Rhonda, Tess, and Alex get back on Interstate 90. At Exit 131 they pick up Badlands Loop. This 32-mile road takes visitors through the heart of Badlands National Park.

The Which Way Wheels roll past beautiful scenery and wildlife. At one point Smart Alex spots a prairie-dog town. Tess stops so that everyone can get a closer look. According to Alex, prairie dogs aren't dogs at all. They are rodents.

You can count on Alex to get his facts right. Speaking of counting, find the total number of prairie dogs in this picture. When you have the exact number, scamper over to the bottom of page 21.

Did you count the number of prairie dogs?
That number is a multiple of one of the numbers below.
Find that number to get your next clue.

Multiple of 8? Cross off Corn Palace and Wind Cave National Park.

Multiple of 7? Cross off Crazy Horse Memorial and Mount Rushmore.

Multiple of 6? Cross off Badlands and Mammoth Site.

Go to page 30 and do what the clue says.

CYCLE CITY

Tess, Rhonda, and Alex head to the Black Hills. Their journey takes them north toward the town of Sturgis. Most of the time Sturgis is a sleepy Black Hills town. But once a year it hosts the biggest motorcycle rally in the world.

When you get to town, the streets are filled with motorcycles and people. Everyone has traveled from somewhere else in South Dakota to get here. You overhear some of their comments. But some of them don't sound right. See if you can pick out which statements are true and which are false. Then roll down to the box on page 23.

> I came from Harney Peak, the highest point in the state.

> I want to swim in Evans Plunge. It's the world's largest natural warm-water indoor swimming pool.

Don't Forget Your Map!
All the information you need for this puzzle can be found on your South Dakota map.

Have you figured out which statements are true?

If two are true, cross off Wind Cave.

If three are true, cross off the Corn Palace.

If none is true, cross off Mammoth Site.

Now turn to page 30 and follow the directions.

Ground Jewels

Noah and Little Bill are also in the Black Hills, but they have traveled west. Noah wants to see Jewel Cave. This enormous cave system is the third longest in the world. It is named for the sparkling crystals on its walls.

Noah and Little Bill decide to explore some of the many caves within Jewel Cave. While they strap on their spelunking gear, you settle down to figure out the next puzzle. Find all the cave names in the word search. They are hidden forward, backward, up, down, and diagonally. When you find them all, go to the box on page 25.

Caves to Explore

ALARM CLOCK
APRIL FOOL AREA
BISHOP
BOOM ROOM
BRAIN DRAIN
COIN SLOT
DEEP SLOT
DISASTER AREA
DIVING BOARD
FEE AREA
GRIEF
HORN
JEWEL BOX
LOG JAM
MOAT
MUD GARDEN
PICNIC AREA
PINHOLE
POOL ROOM
SPITTOON

A E R A R E T S A S I D C
R P I N H O L E O D S M S
O B R A I N D R A I N U F
F S P I T T O O N V T D P
H E P L L A T F E I R G I
T X C E W F A T P N H A C
B O O M R O O M O G F R N
I B L E R L M O O B E D I
S L E S S Y A O L O E E C
H E U P N F J I R A A N A
O W E N D I G B O R R O R
P E N E N R O H O D E E E
D J S K C O L C M R A L A

Did you dig out all the names? Now write the leftover letters in the spaces below. As you write the letters, be sure to go from left to right and from top to bottom of the grid.

___ ___ ___ ___ ___ ___ ___   ___ ___ ___   ___ ___ ___

___ ___ ___ ___ ___ ___   ___ ___ ___ ___ ___ ___   ___ ___

___ ___ ___ ___   ___ ___ ___ ___ ___ .

Now go to page 30 and do what the clue says.

THESE PRESIDENTS ROCK

No trip to South Dakota would be complete without a visit to its most famous site—Mount Rushmore. This majestic sculpture honors four of America's most famous presidents: George Washington, Thomas Jefferson, Theodore Roosevelt, and Abraham Lincoln. Nearly five million people visit this impressive monument every year.

The crew meets as planned near the bottom of Rushmore. As they marvel at the massive sculpture, it's time for you to carve out one final Which Way clue. Fill in the answers. When you're finished, head to the box on page 27.

1. One Native American tribe that lives in South Dakota

_____

2. What Congress established on March 2, 1861

_____

3. State that South Dakota is south of

_____

4. Third-largest city in the state

_____

5. City where gold was discovered

_____

6. Wild West town between the answer to #5 and Sturgis

_____

7. First woman umpire

_____

8. South Dakota's state tree

_____

WHICH WAY USA?

STATE MAP

Don't Forget Your Map!
Your South Dakota map has all the information you need.

Did you discover the answers? There's a clue in the list.
Write the first letter of each answer in the spaces below.

—— —— —— —— —— —— —— ——
1   2   3   4   5   6   7   8

Now read the word from back to front. Go to page 30
and cross that place off the list.

Who?

Which famous South Dakota native is going to be in the Which Way Hall of Fame? Solve the puzzles on pages 2 through 11. Each puzzle will help you eliminate one candidate. When there is only one person left, you will have your answer!

Sparky Anderson
Baseball manager who won World Series titles as skipper of the Cincinnati Reds and the Detroit Tigers

Al Neuharth
Founder of the national newspaper *USA Today* and former chairman of Gannet Company Inc.

Calamity Jane
Army scout and western cowgirl who performed as a sharpshooter in Buffalo Bill Cody's Wild West Show

Zitkala-Sa
Native American writer and politician who founded the National Council of American Indians

Sitting Bull
Hunkpapa Sioux medicine man, chief, and warrior who defeated General Custer at Little Big Horn in Montana

Ernest Lawrence
Scientist and Nobel Prize winner who invented the cyclotron, a device used to break up and study atomic particles

The person going into the Hall of Fame is:

What?

One item from South Dakota will go into the Which Way Museum. To find out what it is, solve the puzzles on pages 12 through 19. Each puzzle will give you a clue. As you solve each puzzle, write a phrase on the lines below. When put together, the phrases will tell you what to do.

Can't Pop This! (pages 12-13)

_____

Sioux Clue (pages 14-15)

_____

Hitting the Wall (pages 16-17)

_____

You Herd That (pages 18-19)

_____

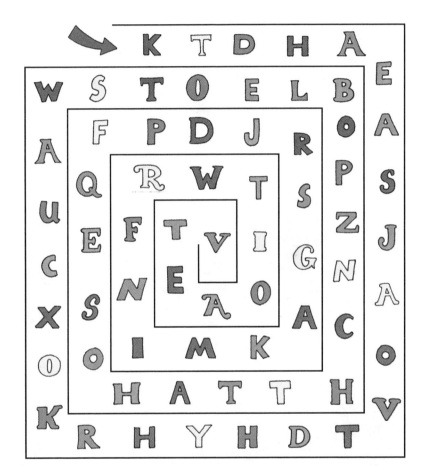

Now write the circled letters in the order that you circled them in the spaces below.

The famous item is:

__ ____ _____ ____

____ _____ ___

Where?

One landmark from South Dakota is to be featured in the Which Way Supermax Movie. To find out where the Which Way cameras are going, solve the puzzles on pages 20 through 27. Each puzzle will help you cross off one or more of the famous places. When you finish, the remaining landmark will be the answer.

Corn Palace
Building in Mitchell artfully decorated with thousands of bushels of grain

Mount Rushmore
One of the most famous national monuments in the United States

Wind Cave National Park
Named for the strong wind that blows through the caverns

Badlands
Rugged, beautiful canyons and gullies in the southwestern part of the state

CRAZY HORSE
1/34th Scale Model
©KORCZAK, Sculptor

Crazy Horse Memorial
A giant sculpture being created to honor all Native Americans

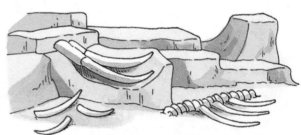

Mammoth Site
Final resting place for the bones of more than 40 prehistoric mammoths

The famous place is:

All the answers for your
Which Way adventure
are on the next two
pages. Do not go

unless you need help
with a puzzle. If you
don't need help,

before you look at
the answers.

You can use the rest of
this page to work out
your puzzles. If you need
a little extra space,

your pencil here. After
you're done, make a

back to the page you
were working on.

ANSWERS

Pages 2-3: **Sioux Falls Calls**

The cup is hidden twice, so cross off Sparky Anderson on page 28.

Pages 4-5: **One in Vermillion**
The code reads

Y O U   C A N   T U N E   O U T

T H E   S C I E N T I S T .

Cross off Ernest Lawrence on page 28.

Pages 6-7: **Li'l Town on the Prairie**
On page 28, cross off ZITKALA-SA.

Pages 8-9: **Town Crossings**

When unscrambled, the letters in the shaded boxes spell THE COWGIRL. Cross off Calamity Jane on page 28.

Pages 10-11: **Once Upon a Time**
1. C I N D E (R) E L L (A)

2. H U M (P) T Y   D U M (P) T Y

3. T H R (E) E   L I T T L E   (P) I G S

4. J A C K   A N D   T H (E)
    B E A (N) S T A L K

5. (S) N O W   (W) H I T E

When unscrambled, the circled letters spell NEWSPAPER. Eliminate Al Neuharth from page 28.

Pages 12-13: **Can't Pop This!**
1. F L A K E S
           1

2. C H I P S
     2

3. M U F F I N
          3

4. O N   T H E   C O B
    4   5

5. C H O W D E R
        6

6. B U T T E R E D   P O P
      7

7. D O G
      8

B E G I N   W I T H
5 1 8 3 4 6 3 7 2

Write the words *BEGIN WITH* in the spaces on page 29.

Pages 14-15: **Sioux Clue**
The basket isn't in the picture, so the clue is: On page 29, write the words *THE FIRST A*.

Pages 16-17: **Hitting the Wall**
Tess spent $19.00, Rhonda spent $19.75, and Alex spent $20.00. Tess had the most money left over ($1.00), so the clue is AND CIRCLE EVERY. Write these three words on page 29.